BARTÓK PIANO COLLECTION
BOOK 1

The
DEFINITIVE
BARTÓK
EDITION

Béla Bartók (signature)

Compiled by Hywel Davies

BOOSEY & HAWKES

Boosey & Hawkes Music Publishers Ltd
www.boosey.com

Published by Boosey & Hawkes Music Publishers Ltd
Aldwych House
71–91 Aldwych
London
WC2B 4HN

www.boosey.com

© Copyright 2016 by Boosey & Hawkes Music Publishers Ltd

ISMN 979-0-060-13198-1
ISBN 978-1-78454-192-7

First impression 2016

Printed by Halstan:
Halstan UK, 2-10 Plantation Road, Amersham, Bucks, HP6 6HJ. United Kingdom
Halstan DE, Weißliliengasse 4, 55116 Mainz. Germany

Compiled by Hywel Davies
Music origination by Jon Bunker
Cover design by Chloë Alexander Design (chloealexanderdesign.dphoto.com)
Piano performance by Iain Farrington

BARTÓK PIANO COLLECTION
BOOK 1

FULL PERFORMANCE CD

 The enclosed CD contains demonstration tracks for all pieces in this book performed by Iain Farrington. Track numbers are shown in black circles.

BÉLA BARTÓK

Béla Bartók was born in the Hungarian town of Nagyszentmiklós (now Sînnicolau Mare in Romania) on 25 March 1881, and received his first music lessons from his mother. When his family moved he took further lessons in Pressburg (now Bratislava in Slovakia) before becoming a student at the Royal Academy of Music in Budapest – graduating in 1903. He began to establish an international reputation as a fine pianist, and was soon drawn into teaching: in 1907 he became professor of piano at the Academy.

Bartók's earliest compositions offer a blend of late Romanticism and nationalist elements, formed under the influences of Wagner, Brahms, Liszt and Strauss. Around 1905 his friend and fellow-composer Zoltán Kodály directed his attention to Hungarian folk music and – coupled with his discovery of the music of Debussy – Bartók's musical language changed dramatically. As he absorbed more and more of the spirit of Hungarian folk songs and dances, his own music grew more concentrated, chromatic and dissonant. Although a sense of key is sometimes lost in individual passages, Bartók never espoused atonality as a compositional technique.

Bartók's interest is folk music was not merely passive: he was an assiduous ethnomusicologist, and undertook his first systematic collecting trips in Hungary with Kodály. Thereafter Bartók's interest and involvement grew deeper and his scope wider, encompassing a number of ethnic traditions both near at hand and further afield: Transylvanian, Romanian, North African and others.

In the 1920s and '30s Bartók's international fame spread, and he toured widely, both as pianist (usually in his own works) and as a respected composer. Works like *Dance Suite* for orchestra (1923) and *Divertimento* for strings (1939) maintained his high profile. He continued to teach at the Academy of Music until his resignation in 1934, devoting much of his free time thereafter to his ethnomusicological research.

With the outbreak of the Second World War, and despite his deep attachment to his homeland, life in Hungary became intolerable and Bartók emigrated to the United States. Here his material conditions worsened considerably, despite initial promise: although he obtained a post at Columbia University and was able to pursue his folk-music studies, his concert engagements become very much rarer. He received few commissions, so the request for a Concerto for Orchestra (1943) was therefore particularly important, bringing him much-needed income. Bartók died following a period of ill health on 26 September 1945.

ST GEORGE'S DAY

For Children – book I, no 2

01

BÉLA BARTÓK
(1881–1945)

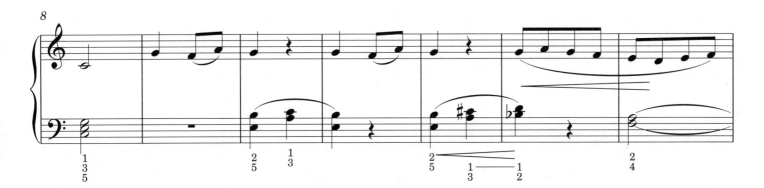

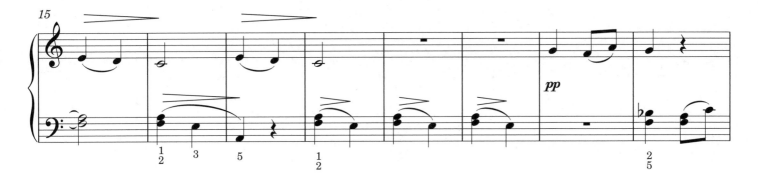

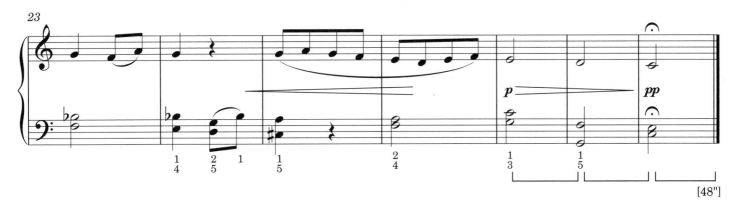

[48"]

For Children (1908–1909, and later revised) is a two-volume collection of folk song transcriptions and arrangements which Bartók created for piano teaching. Volume I contains songs of Hungarian origin, whilst the music in volume II is Slovakian.

The song words for this Hungarian song are translated *'Come out, sun, for Saint George's Day! Little lamb on the green nearly dies with cold.'*

COME HOME, LIDI

For Children – book I, no 3

BÉLA BARTÓK
(1881–1945)

[45"]

This Hungarian melody is written in the Dorian mode on A. The words are translated: *'I've lost my mate, my pretty marriageable daughter. Come home, my daughter called Lidi.'*

MELODY WITH ACCOMPANIMENT

Mikrokosmos – no 41

BÉLA BARTÓK
(1881–1945)

[40"]

Mikrokosmos (1926–1939) is a collection of 153 pieces which Bartók wrote for students to assist them in navigating their way through some of the 'most important technical and musical problems' faced by developing pianists. It is considered one of the most significant pedagogical works for piano written in the twentieth century.

This piece has an unusual key signature and is written using a combination of Lydian and Mixolydian modes.

CHILDREN'S SONG

For Children – book II, no 9

04

BÉLA BARTÓK
(1881–1945)

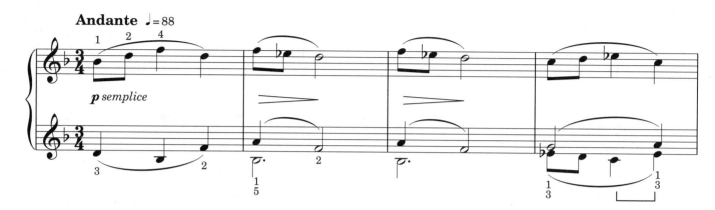

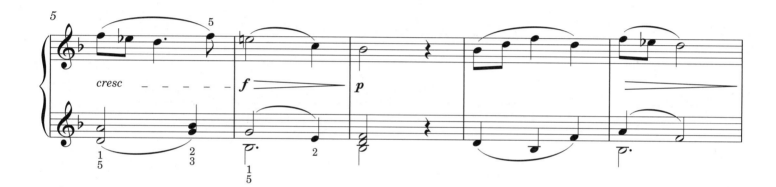

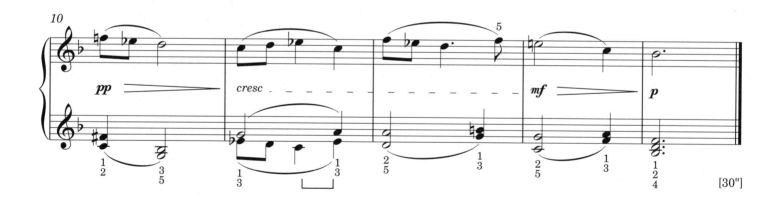

[30"]

This Slovakian folk song has a B♭ major key centre, but becomes Lydian at the end of phrases. The melody in the right hand should sound lilting and graceful over a sweet and delicate left hand accompaniment.

The song words are translated: *'Unfold yourself, blossom, you green shrubs of the island.'*

This edition © Copyright 2016 by Boosey & Hawkes Music Publishers Ltd

MOURNING SONG

For Children – book II, no 10

BÉLA BARTÓK
(1881–1945)

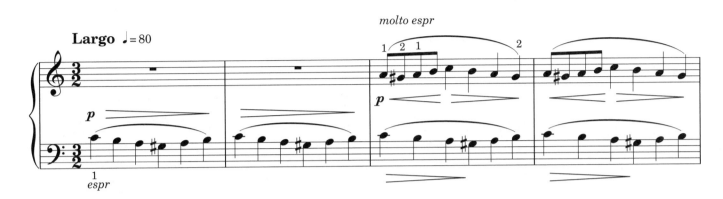

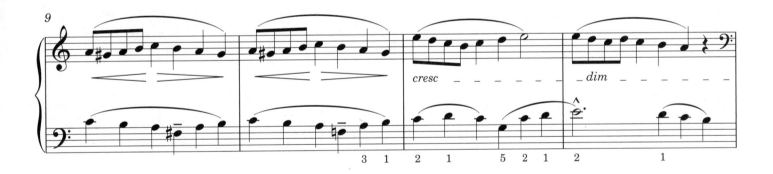

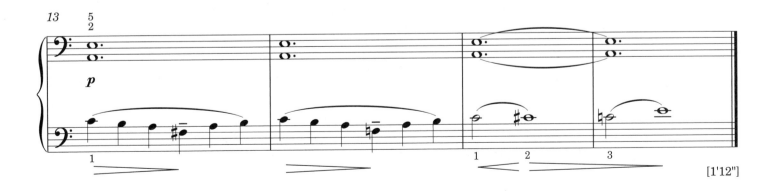

[1'12"]

This Slovakian funeral song should be played with great sensitivity. Its words are translated: *'In the barracks of Mikuláš my dead lover is laid out; he lies full of wounds, covered with rosemary.'*

6

IN YUGOSLAV STYLE

Mikrokosmos – no 40

(1881–1945)

06

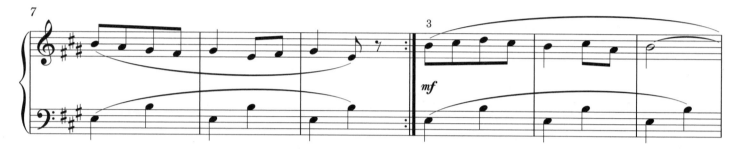

[40"]

An imitation of Yugoslovian bagpipe music in mixolydian mode on E, where the left hand imitates a drone and the right hand carries a chanter-like melody.

PLOUGHING

For Children – book II, no 14

BÉLA BARTÓK
(1881–1945)

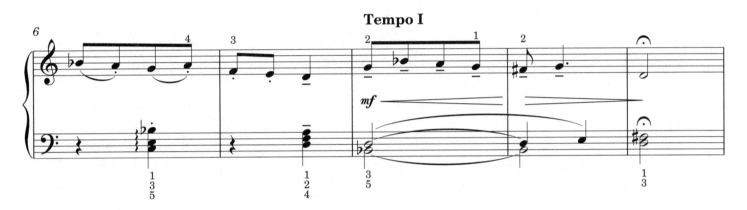

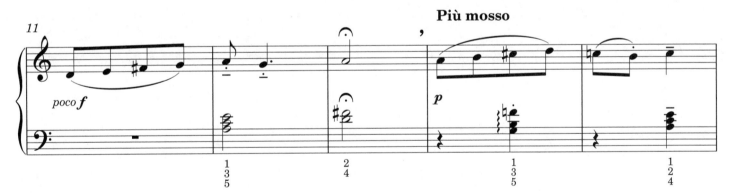

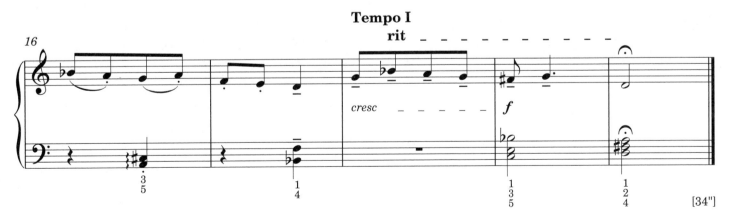

[34"]

A right hand melody with left hand chordal accompaniment.

This Slovakian song is translated: *'On a pine-topped hill there are six oxen. Four are ploughing, two harrowing; who is driving them?'*

ROGUE'S SONG / SORROW

For Children – book II, no 7

BÉLA BARTÓK
(1881–1945)

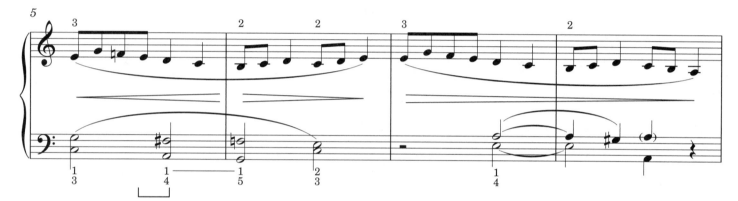

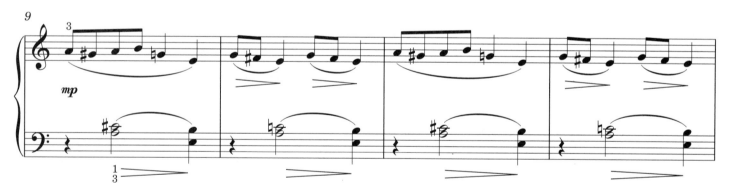

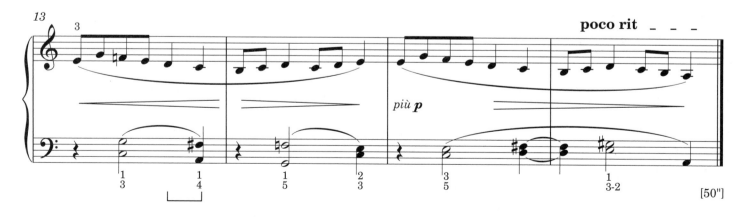

[50"]

This Slovakian song tells the story of a soldier (the 'rogue') who is witnessed committing a heinous crime after returning from war in Poland. He is sentenced to death but his life is spared: *'The sheriff wanted to hang me, but there were girls there who did not allow it.'*

This edition © Copyright 2016 by Boosey & Hawkes Music Publishers Ltd

BAGATELLE №6

Fourteen Bagatelles

BÉLA BARTÓK
(1881–1945)

Bartok described his set of *Fourteen Bagatelles* (1908) as representing *'a new piano style [which was] a reaction to the exuberance of the Romantic piano music of the nineteenth century… stripped of all unessential decorative elements, deliberately using only the most restricted technical means.'* In this, the sixth piece in the collection, the melody and two-voice left-hand accompaniment presents a study in **legato** playing. The accompaniment should sound very smooth and sustained – without use of the pedal.

BAKING SONG

For Children – book I, no 1

BÉLA BARTÓK
(1881–1945)

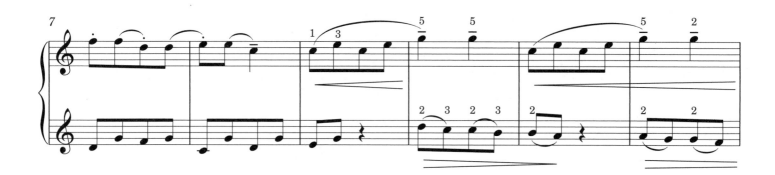

[32"]

A study in playing contrasting phrasing, articulation and dynamics in each hand.

The words of this Hungarian piece are translated: *'Let's bake something made of flour with filling – a snail-shaped strudel, round and sweet!'*

This edition © Copyright 2016 by Boosey & Hawkes Music Publishers Ltd

COUNTY FAIR

Mikrokosmos – no 47

BÉLA BARTÓK
(1881–1945)

Written in the Dorian mode on A, this lively and boisterous piece requires lots of attack and measured use of the pedal. Voices move in contrary motion in broken thirds and fourths creating an exciting fair-like atmosphere.

[35"]

THE LOST COUPLE

For Children – book I, no 11

BÉLA BARTÓK
(1881–1945)

Using the same text as '*Come home, Lidi*' (page 2), this piece has a D major key signature. The melody and accompaniment switch hands at bars 13 and 24.

This edition © Copyright 2016 by Boosey & Hawkes Music Publishers Ltd

THE TWO ROSES

For Children – book II, no 3

BÉLA BARTÓK
(1881–1945)

⑬

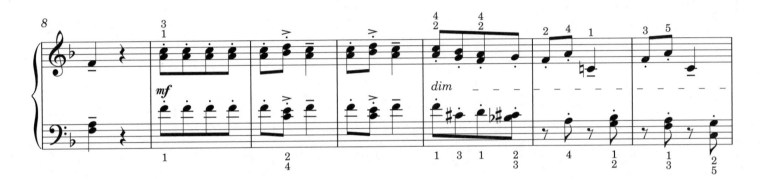

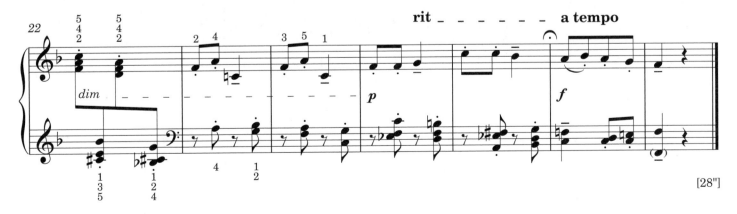

[28"]

The text of this Slovakian song is translated: *That girl gave me one of two roses by the tree. "Give me the other one, because it means love." "I won't give it, because there'll be none left for me!"* Approach this teasing piece playfully.

This edition © Copyright 2016 by Boosey & Hawkes Music Publishers Ltd

THREE ROSES

For Children – book II, no 11

BÉLA BARTÓK
(1881–1945)

[1']
attacca
(ad lib)

MY LOVER'S MOTHER

For Children – book II, no 12

BÉLA BARTÓK
(1881–1945)

[40"]
attacca
(ad lib)

WHERE ARE YOUR GEESE?

For Children – book II, no 13

BÉLA BARTÓK
(1881–1945)

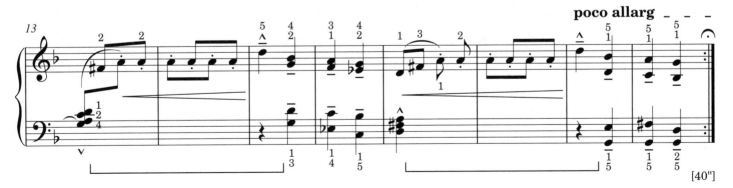

[40"]

A triptych of Slovakian folk songs which can be played separately or as a set – a celebration of the fragrance of roses, a plea to the mother of a lover not to curse their path, and a tale of a shirt-soaking trip into water to fetch some straying geese!

SLOVAKIAN FOLK SONG

Ten Easy Pieces – no 8

BÉLA BARTÓK
(1881–1945)

Composed in 1908 and designed as a companion volume to the *Fourteen Bagatelles*, *Ten Easy Pieces* demonstrates a variety of styles which were influential to Bartók at the time.

Based on a folk song called *Kopala studienku*, this melody forms part of the Slovakian national anthem.

This edition © Copyright 2016 by Boosey & Hawkes Music Publishers Ltd

IN THE GARDEN

For Children – book I, no 26

BÉLA BARTÓK
(1881–1945)

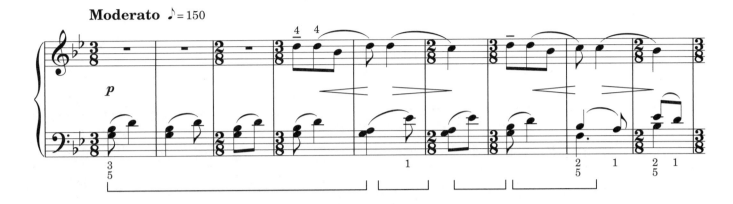

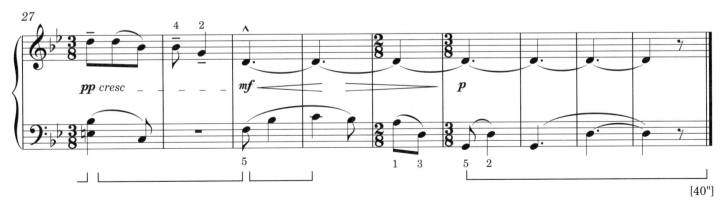

[40"]

A hungarian folk song: *'Sweetheart, go around my garden, don't be grief stricken.'*

In its original form this piece was written entirely within a ³/₈ time signature. In 1943, Bartok made a number of revisions to the pieces in *For Children* and chose to add the ³/₈ ³/₈ fluctuation in this piece as shown above. Both versions have a beautiful sombre elegance.

CAROL No 4

Romanian Christmas Carols – set II

(19)

BÉLA BARTÓK
(1881–1945)

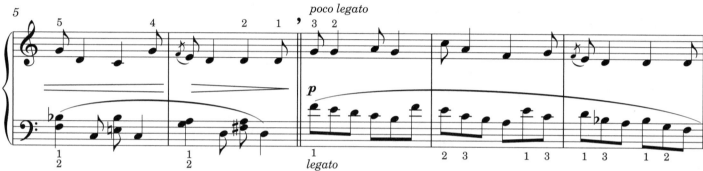

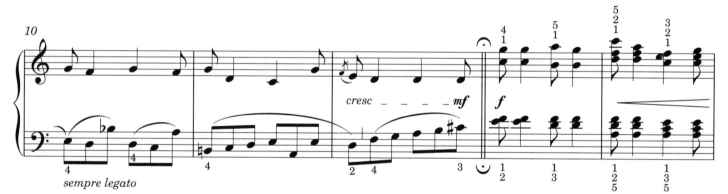

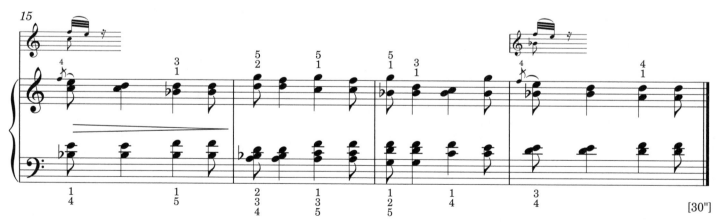

[30"]

The twenty original songs collected by Bartók (published in two volumes in 1915) would have been sung by young Romanian carol singers on Christmas Eve. Many of the texts are based on Christian liturgy; some are of a pagan origin.

The fourth carol in set II is translated: *'Let us come inside, for outside the rain is pouring and our horses have gone lame, and they should be shod anew with horseshoes of pastry and nails of sausage. Get up, host; give them to us!* [Refrain:] *Unto the Lord God Almighty!'*

CAROL № 7

Romanian Christmas Carols – set II

BÉLA BARTÓK
(1881–1945)

⟨20⟩

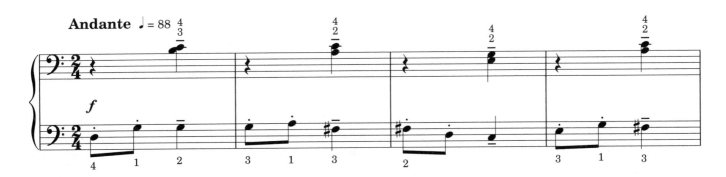

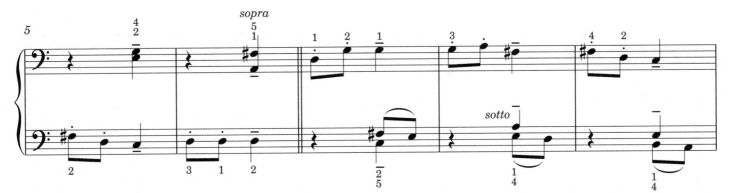

[25"]

A variation of a previous carol in set II, this piece contains three variations of a melody voiced in different registers. In the first two variations the left and right hand play in extremely close proximity and sometimes overlap.

The original Romanian text is translated: *'At the quiet well-spring the Lord God and the Virgin Mary and a small Son were resting.'*

TRIPLETS

Mikrokosmos – no 75

(21)

BÉLA BARTÓK
(1881–1945)

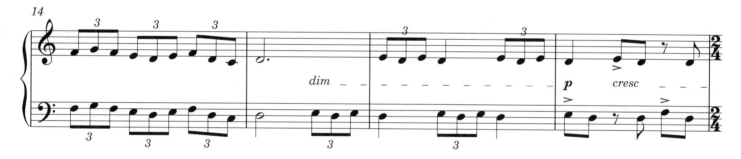

[54"]

An exploration of triplet versus duplet rhythms with shifting metres. A strong crotchet pulse should be felt throughout.

FAREWELL

For Children – book II, no 34

BÉLA BARTÓK
(1881–1945)

This Slovakian song of parting is translated: *'I look back upon you once more, mountain of Zvolen; I would like to speak to you once more, darling.'* Let the haunting melody remain in the foreground and ensure the accompaniment is played delicately with all of its subtle and intricate dynamic variation.

DUET FOR PIPES

Mikrokosmos – no 88

BÉLA BARTÓK
(1881–1945)

Two pipes or flutes play chromatic melodies with skips and jumps, dominated by triplet rhythms. The lines at the end of bar 22 denote an interruption of *legato*.

KITTY, KITTY

For Children – book I, no 5

BÉLA BARTÓK
(1881–1945)

A melody with chordal accompaniment in C major. The Hungarian song is a nonsense song, whose words are translated, ' "Kitty, kitty, have you a pretty girl?"
"I have, I have, but what is it good for?" "Give her to me, I take her!" Sieve, sieve Friday, love Thursday, drum Wednesday.'

ROUND DANCE

For Children – book I, no 17

BÉLA BARTÓK
(1881–1945)

A serene melody over swaying accompaniment in Aeolian mode on E.

[1']

The text of the Hungarian folk song is translated: *'My lovely girl is dressed in white; turn to me, you married bride.'*

BAGATELLE № 4

Fourteen Bagatelles

BÉLA BARTÓK
(1881–1945)

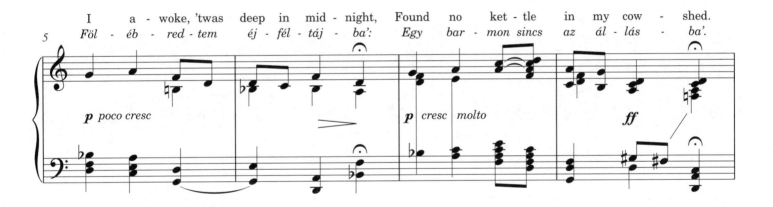

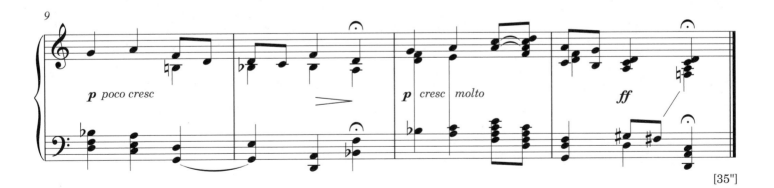

[35"]

Predominantly chordal textures in an arrangement of a Hungarian folksong in Aeolian mode on D. There is a considerable dynamic range and up to eight concurrent voices in each chord.

This edition © Copyright 2016 by Boosey & Hawkes Music Publishers Ltd

VARIATIONS

Mikrokosmos – no 87

BÉLA BARTÓK
(1881–1945)

Theme with two variations. The melody and accompaniment frequently fluctuate between hands. There is a Dorian modal feel (on D) but regular use of the D major chord at cadences. The final chord of the piece is notably (and somewhat unusually) a second inversion chord of D major.

This edition © Copyright 2016 by Boosey & Hawkes Music Publishers Ltd

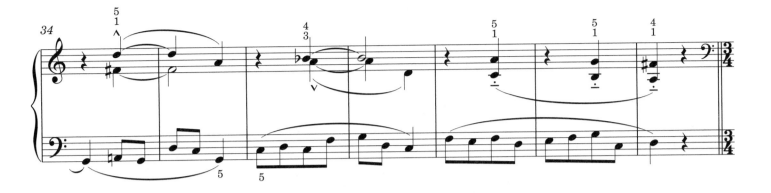

Lo stesso tempo (♩ = 138), **tranquillo**

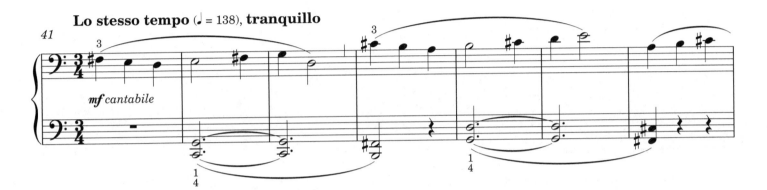

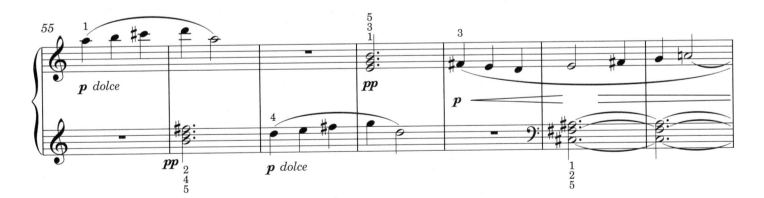

Più andante ♩ = 160

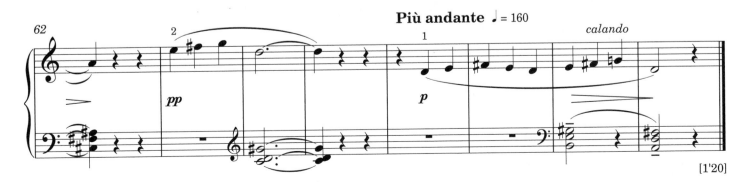

[1'20]

FROM THE ISLAND OF BALI

Mikrokosmos – no 109

BÉLA BARTÓK
(1881–1945)

An impressionistic composition evoking the festive atmosphere of a tropical island. The **Risoluto** section might represent a dance.

The *prol* 🎹 markings at the end of bars 29 and 39 indicate the held notes (low D in bar 29, A and D in bar 40) can be sustained with the solo *sostenuto* (sustaining) pedal. (Where there are three pedals on a piano, this is sometimes the pedal at the centre).

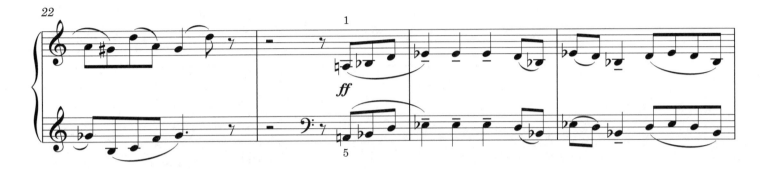

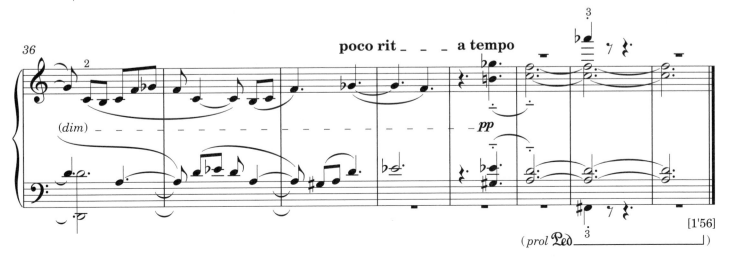

[1'56]

CHILDREN'S DANCE

For Children – book I, no 10

BÉLA BARTÓK
(1881–1945)

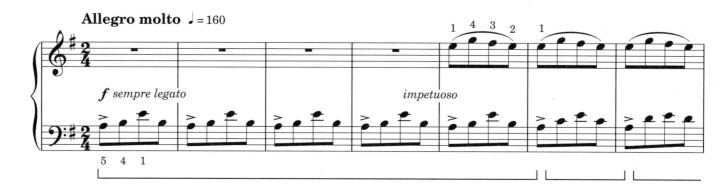

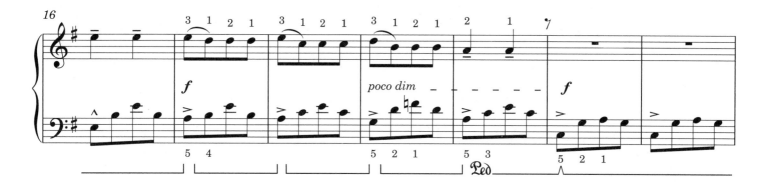

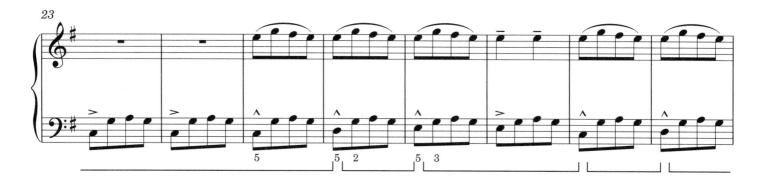

The right hand plays the melody over a continous left hand ostinato in Dorian mode on A.

The folk song text is translated: *'A good time is had by those who walk in twos. See! I, poor journeyman, walk by myself...'*

[40"]

Also available from Boosey & Hawkes

FOR CHILDREN (Definitive Edition)
Béla Bartók

ISMN 979-0-060-11230-0 (volume 1)
ISMN 979-0-060-11231-7 (volume 2)

40 Hungarian tunes (volume 1) and 39 Slovakian tunes (volume 2) for beginner pianists in a revised and re-engraved edition.

Includes an introductory note by the composer's son, Peter Bartók.

MIKROKOSMOS (Definitive Edition)
Béla Bartók

English, Japanese, Spanish & Portuguese
Book 1: ISMN 979-0-060-09731-7
Book 2: ISMN 979-0-060-09732-4
Book 3: ISMN 979-0-060-09733-1
Book 4: ISMN 979-0-060-09734-8
Book 5: ISMN 979-0-060-09735-5
Book 6: ISMN 979-0-060-09736-2

English, French, German & Hungarian
Book 1: ISMN 979-0-060-08001-2
Book 2: ISMN 979-0-060-08002-9
Book 3: ISMN 979-0-060-08003-6
Book 4: ISMN 979-0-060-08004-3
Book 5: ISMN 979-0-060-08005-0
Book 6: ISMN 979-0-060-08006-7

Béla Bartók described *Mikrokosmos* as a cycle of 153 compositions for piano written for 'didactic' purposes – a series of short pieces in many different styles, representing a small world, or the 'world of the little ones, the children'. Stylistically, *Mikrokosmos* reflects the influence of folk music on Bartók's life, and the rhythms and harmonies employed create music that is as modern today as when the cycle was first written.

Mikrokosmos is available in six progressive volumes. An introductory note by Peter Bartók is included in each volume.

BOOSEY & HAWKES

AN IMAGEM COMPANY

AD 508